THE CHRONICLES OF JUDGE DREDD by Pat Mills, Mike McMal

CW01022324

THE CURSED EARTH
PART ONE

TITAN BOOKS

INTRODUCTION

The Cursed Earth remains to this day the most ambitious *Judge Dredd* story yet conceived. Comprising twenty five episodes and over 150 pages of artwork, which ran in Progs 61-85 of the IPC sf weekly comic, *2000 AD*, it is all the more remarkable for the fact that only two artists — Mike McMahon (18 chapters) and Brian Bolland (7 chapters) — worked on it. The writing was handled by Pat Mills, creator and former editor of *2000 AD*, assisted by John Wagner on four chapters and Jack Adrian on two. This second volume in *The Chronicles of Judge Dredd* contains the first half of *The Cursed Earth*, for which Brian Bolland has drawn *three new pages* to provide visual continuity. *The Cursed Earth* will be completed in volume three.

The story concerns Judge Dredd, *2000 AD's* most popular hero, and his vital mission to deliver a precious cargo of life-saving vaccine across the treacherous wastelands of the Cursed Earth to the plague-ridden inhabitants of Mega-City Two. Writer Pat Mills removed Dredd from his normal Mega-City One beat which he considered to be more the scripting province of regular John Wagner, and gave Dredd two major protagonists, Spikes Harvey Rotten and Tweak. Spikes was an anarchistic 'Johnny Rotten' style punk who hated the world and everything that Dredd stood for, and acted as both his companion and foil. Mills pulled Rotten from an earlier Dredd story *The Mega-City 5000* — Progs 41 & 42, Brian Bolland's first artwork on the series and fleshed out his character, giving him a new, and more appropriate visual appearance. Tweak was an 'original'. Mills had never felt happy writing Walter, Dredd's regular companion, but wanted a character that the readers could sympathise with and that could get beaten up, tortured and shot at — and still come out alive! When he spotted an incredible looking creature called a Tamandua (a Peruvian anteater) in an issue of National Geographic, he knew he had the answer.

The other subsidiary characters — three judges and three war droids — came along as cannon fodder. Mills was so enthusiastic about disposing of his creations that he even named the first Cursed Earth casualty — Assistant Grand Judge *Fodder*! Even Dredd underwent character changes — from a relentless, macho city cop, who could only cope with the insanity of Mega City One by being tougher and more ruthless than its inhabitants, to a fairer, more compassionate lawman whose treatment of the Cursed Earth mutants was both sympathetic and just.

Above: Spikes Harvey Rotten as he appears in Mega-City 5000 (Prog 41).

The Cursed Earth lay between two giant Mega-Cities, represented by modern day New York State and California, which meant that Dredd's East to West route had to make geographical sense. This caused some problems. Mills had been determined to introduce a story concerning Mount Rushmore and the president's heads as early as possible, but after having plotted it he discovered the site was a lot further west than he'd hoped. He didn't want to change his story, so he changed America. He wrote in an extra paragraph explaining how Rushmore had been relocated to just outside Mega-City One on the premise that sightseers and tourists wouldn't have to travel so far to see it.

The Cursed Earth represented a high point in Dredd's popularity with the readers, his highest ever votes coming from the Satanus stories (which appear in *Book Two*). Judge Dredd has now made his mark in comic history, having won Eagle Awards — fandom's highest accolade — in many categories every year.

NICK LANDAU, December 1981

PAT MILLS *has been responsible for creating some of Britain's most exciting comics, notably –* 2000 AD, Action *and* Battle. *As a writer, he has inspired the best work of many artists and has created hundreds of entertaining stories, including* Robusters, ABC Warriors, Nemesis *and* Slaine *for* 2000 AD *as well as* Charley's War *for* Battle, Metalzoic *for DC Comics and* You are Margaret Thatcher – a Dole Playing Game *for Titan Books, Pat is currently working with Glenn Fabry on* Scatha *for* News on Sunday *and with Kevin O'Neill on* Marshal Law *for Epic Comics.*

MIKE McMAHON *has helped create definitive images for many of the characters he has drawn, particularly* Judge Dredd *and the* ABC Warriors. *His substantial body of work also includes* Slaine *and covers for* Judge Dredd Monthly, *published in the USA for Eagle Comics.*

BRIAN BOLLAND's *professional comics career began in 1974, and since then the quality of his artwork and his popularity have increased meteorically. He has become most renowned for his work on* Judge Dredd *in* 2000 AD *in the UK, and on* Camelot 3000 *for DC Comics in the USA. He is currently drawing a* Batman-Joker *graphic novel for DC Comics.*

Published by Titan Books Ltd, 58 St Giles High St, London WC2H 8LH, England. Distributed in the United Kingdom and the United States of America by Titan Distributors Ltd, P.O. Box 250, London E3 4RT, England. *Judge Dredd* is © IPC Magazines Ltd, 1987. This edition is © Titan Books Ltd, 1987. Printed in England. ISBN 0 907610 01 3. *First edition 1982.*
10 9 8 7 6 5

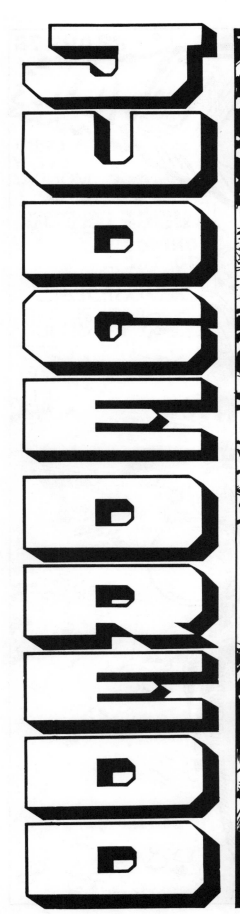

2000 A.D.
Credit Card:

SCRIPT ROBOT
PAT MILLS
ART ROBOT
MIKE McMAHON
LETTERING ROBOT
TOM FRAME

COMPU·73E

NEVER A DULL MOMENT WHEN YOU'RE A **TWENTY-SECOND CENTURY COP!**

CHAPTER ONE:
FORBIDDEN FRUIT!

SPECIAL SECURITY WING, JUSTICE H.Q., MEGA-CITY ONE. **JUDGE DREDD** IS CALLED OFF PATROL TO MEET AN OLD FRIEND...

HELLO, RED. LONG TIME — NO SEE. HEAR YOU GOT A **HELLUVA** STORY TO TELL ME.

HELL IS THE RIGHT WORD, JUDGE...

FOOD STERILE UNIT

QUAR-BUB 55

IN CHARGE OF THE WING — ASSISTANT GRAND JUDGE FODDER...

YOU'LL HAVE TO EXCUSE RED BEING INSIDE THE **PLASTIC BUBBLE**, JUDGE. HIS PERIOD OF QUARANTINE IS NOT YET UP.

BUT HE HAS EVERY COMFORT... MUSIC...TV...

CAN **WE** GET ON WITH IT? IN THE TIME I'VE WASTED WITH YOU, JUDGE FODDER, I COULD HAVE ARRESTED **FIVE** LAW-BREAKERS!

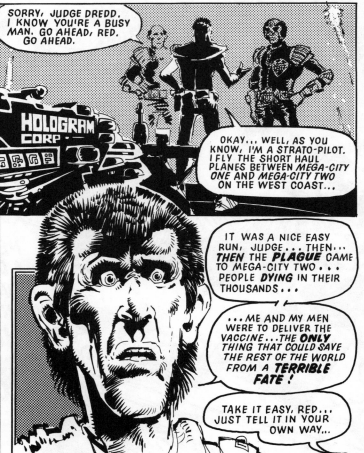

SORRY, JUDGE DREDD. I KNOW YOU'RE A BUSY MAN. GO AHEAD, RED. GO AHEAD.

HOLOGRAM CORP

OKAY... WELL, AS YOU KNOW, I'M A STRATO-PILOT. I FLY THE SHORT HAUL PLANES BETWEEN **MEGA-CITY ONE** AND **MEGA-CITY TWO** ON THE WEST COAST...

IT WAS A NICE EASY RUN, JUDGE...THEN... THEN THE **PLAGUE** CAME TO MEGA-CITY TWO... PEOPLE **DYING** IN THEIR THOUSANDS...

...ME AND MY MEN WERE TO DELIVER THE VACCINE...THE **ONLY** THING THAT COULD SAVE THE REST OF THE WORLD FROM A **TERRIBLE FATE!**

TAKE IT EASY, RED... JUST TELL IT IN YOUR OWN WAY...

ONLY *ONE* SECTION OF MEGA-CITY TWO IS HOLDING OUT. IT DESPERATELY NEEDS THAT VACCINE.

WITH THE AIRPORTS IN THE PLAGUE MEN'S HANDS, THERE'S ONLY *ONE* OTHER WAY...

...*BY LAND!* AND THAT'S WHERE I COME IN, HUH?

FORGET IT! TO SURVIVE *THE CURSED EARTH,* A THOUSAND MILES OF MAN-MADE HELL, I'D NEED *SPECIAL* MEN...A *SPECIAL* MACHINE...

WE GOT THEM, DREDD...IF *YOU'LL* DO IT...

HUUUH...? MY HANDS...? *WHAT'S* HAPPENING...?

TOOTY...?

YOUR SURVIVAL CHANCES ARE *LOW*...BUT IT'S *GOT* TO BE TRIED...

...FOR THE FUTURE OF CIVILISATION..!

...IS IN YOUR HANDS!
AAAGH!

TOOTY FRUITY!

HE'S STRANGLING HIM... HE'S TURNED INTO A PLAGUE MAN!

WANT... MUST HAVE... FORBIDDEN FRUIT!

HE-HE'S *SHOVING* THE ASSISTANT GRAND JUDGE THROUGH HIS *FOOD STERILISATION CHAMBER!*

MUST HAVE!

FOOD STERILE UNIT

STAND BACK, DREDD. *THERE'S NO REASONING WITH HIM...* I'LL *BLAST* THE GOOK TO KINGDOM COME!

NO! IF YOU BURST THAT BUBBLE, THE DISEASE WILL *SPREAD* INTO THE MEGA-CITY! I'LL HANDLE THIS.

THE CURSED EARTH
CHAPTER TWO
INTO THE DARKNESS

JUDGE DREDD IS ABOUT TO BEGIN A *DESPERATE* RESCUE MISSION TO MEGA-CITY TWO, ACROSS THE *CURSED EARTH* — A STRETCH OF RADIOACTIVE WASTELAND LEFT OVER FROM THE ATOMIC WARS...

JUDGE DREDD

...NOW, AT THE VEHICLE TESTING GROUND, JUSTICE H.Q....

THERE'S YOUR VEHICLE, DREDD... THE NEW *K2001 LAND RAIDER!* IT'S GOT FOUR WHEEL DRIVE, THERMO-NUCLEAR ENGINE, FLAME THROWER, MACHINE GUNS AND A SPECIAL COMPARTMENT FOR CARRYING THE ANTI-PLAGUE VACCINE!

H'MM! LOOKS SLEEK AND FAST. BUT I'LL NEED SOMETHING *BIGGER* AND *TOUGHER* IF I'M GONNA GET THE VACCINE TO MEGA-CITY TWO.

HOLD IT, DREDD — YOU'VE ONLY SEEN *HALF* THE LAND RAIDER YET! TAKE A LOOK OVER THERE, I THINK YOU'LL LIKE...

...THE KILLDOZER!

A DETACHMENT OF THOSE WAR DROIDS WILL BE GOING WITH YOU, DREDD. THEY'RE RATHER STUPID — CAN'T TALK MUCH, BUT THEY DO THEIR JOB.

H'MM... AFTER WALTER—THAT'LL BE A NICE CHANGE!

}PANT{ }PANT{ WE'VE ALSO SELECTED THREE OF OUR TOP JUDGES TO ASSIST YOU, JUDGE JACK, JUDGE PATTON AND JUDGE GRADGRIND. }GASP{

GOOD TO HAVE YOU WITH ME, GENTLEMEN. WE FOUGHT TOGETHER IN THE ROBOT REBELLION, I BELIEVE, JUDGE JACK.

THIS IS YOUR ROUTE TO MEGA CITY TWO...ACROSS A THOUSAND MILES OF THE CURSED EARTH. YOU'LL HAVE TO FACE MUTIES, SLAY-RIDERS, AND OTHER NAMELESS HORRORS CAUSED BY THE ATOMIC WARS.

IT'S CRAZY... MAN WITH HIS HYPER-TECHNOLOGY CAN TRAVEL TO THE MOON AND BEYOND — YET HE'S STILL MADE A REAL MESS OF HIS HOME PLANET.

YOU ALSO NEED A BIKE MAN FOR THE SECOND QUASAR BIKE, DREDD. I SUGGEST—

NO! I'LL PICK MY OWN BIKER! HE'S GOT TO BE SOMEONE SPECIAL. AND I KNOW JUST THE MAN...

DREDD CLIMBED ABOARD HIS CITY-BIKE...

GET ME THE GOVERNOR OF THE MEGA-PENITENTIARY. I'M ON MY WAY TO VISIT ONE OF HIS HIGH RISK PRISONERS...

VEHICLE TESTING CENTRE

SPIKES HARVEY ROTTEN!

THE GOVERNOR APPEARED ON DREDD'S VID-COM...

SPIKES HARVEY ROTTEN? HE'S A *REFORMED* CHARACTER NOW, JUDGE. AT THIS MOMENT HE'S VISITING *MEGA-SCHOOL THREE* — TELLING THE KIDS HOW TERRIBLE IT IS TO BE A *LAWBREAKER*.

YOU SEE, SPIKES WANTED TO DO SOMETHING *GOOD* WITH HIS LIFE. WE *REFORM* NINETY NINE PER CENT OF OUR PRISONERS HERE, YOU KNOW.

IT'S THE OTHER ONE PER CENT I'M WORRIED ABOUT, GOVERNOR.

GOT TO GET TO MEGA-SCHOOL THREE... FAST.

AT THAT MOMENT, AT MEGA-SCHOOL THREE...

DON'T END UP LIKE ME, KIDS. I'M A LAWBREAKER! I'M DIRT! DERE AIN'T A SCRAP OF DECENCY IN ME!

SOMETIMES, WHEN I WAKE UP IN DA MORNING, KIDS... I LOOK AT MYSELF IN THE MIRROR AND I WANNA BE *SICK!*

WIPE DAT SMILE OFF YER FACE, KID! BEING A LAWBREAKER AIN'T NOTHIN' TO SMILE ABOUT! IT'S DUMB! D'YOU HEAR?

JUST LIKE WEARIN' DESE HANDCUFFS IS DUMB...

BOY... SPIKES IS REALLY TELLING IT FROM THE HEART... HE'S EVEN GOT ME CHOKED UP!

JUST LIKE DIS WARDER IS DUMB! HURR, HURRR!

zit sié

UUUGHH CHOKE GAKKK

MEANWHILE, DREDD ARRIVES AT MEGA-SCHOOL THREE...

I ONLY HOPE I'M IN TIME...

18

THE CURSED EARTH.
CHAPTER 3:

THE DEVIL'S LAPDOGS

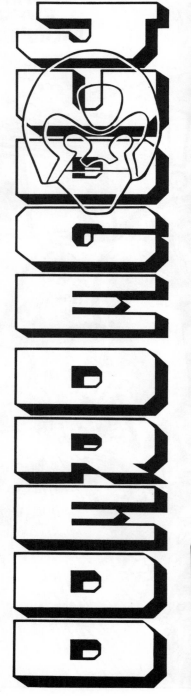

IN THE TOWN OF **DELIVERANCE**, IN THE CURSED EARTH, A STRETCH OF RADIO-ACTIVE WASTELAND LEFT OVER FROM THE ATOMIC WARS, A GRIM **EXECUTION** IS SHORTLY TO TAKE PLACE...

TOWNSFOLK SAMUEL AND REBECCA, YOU HAVE BEEN FOUND **GUILTY** OF STEALING FOOD FROM YOUR NEIGHBOURS.

HAVE YOU ANYTHING TO SAY BEFORE THE **SENTENCE IS CARRIED OUT...?**

2000 A.D.
Credit Card:
SCRIPT ROBOT
PAT MILLS
ART ROBOT
MIKE McMAHON
LETTERING ROBOT
R. O. BOTT
COMPU·73E

MEANWHILE, THE LAND-RAIDER IS PLUNGING ACROSS THE CURSED EARTH ON A RESCUE MISSION TO MEGA-CITY TWO.

ON BOARD, A CREW OF JUDGES AND ROBOTS AND A LAWBREAKER — SPIKES HARVEY ROTTEN...

THAT'S FIVE MILLION CREDITS YOU OWE ME NOW, SPIKES! PAY UP!

I AIN'T PAYIN' YOU NOTHIN', JUDGE JACK!

HEY, I DON'T REMEMBER THAT "CHANCE" CARD IN THE PACK! HERE — LET'S HAVE A LOOK, YOU CHEAT!

WHY SHOULD I? AND, TALKIN' OF CHEATIN', I DON'T REMEMBER YOU LANDIN' ON ANY OF MY SPACE PORTS!

WHY YOU....!

IF YOU GENTLEMEN HAVE QUITE FINISHED!

JUDGE DREDD, THEIR LEADER, SPEAKS...

MAY I REMIND YOU THAT WE ARE ON A VITAL MISSION TO MEGA-CITY TWO. IF WE DON'T GET THROUGH WITH THE VACCINE, THOUSANDS WILL DIE!

SPIKES! YOU AND ME ARE GOING OUT ON A RECCE ON THE QUASAR BIKES!

THE CURSED EARTH
CHAPTER 4.

THE TOWN OF DELIVERANCE, IN THE CURSED EARTH, IS IN TROUBLE... *BIG TROUBLE!* IT IS BEING ATTACKED BY A RAIN OF FLYING RATS—AND JUST ONE BITE FROM THE RATS IS... *CERTAIN DEATH!*

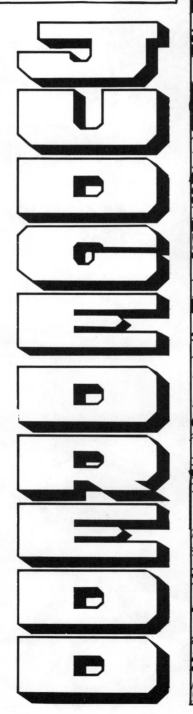

2000 A.D.
Credit Card:

SCRIPT ROBOT
PAT MILLS

ART ROBOT
MIKE McMAHON

LETTERING ROBOT
TOM FRAME

COMPU·73E

SECONDS TICKED BY, THEN...

ITS FUR'S ON END... *LEAPING FOR MY FACE!* GOTTA —

— GRAB ITS THROAT AND... *SQUEEZE THE ...LIFE OUT...OF IT!*

THE FINAL BATTLE OVER, DREDD AND SPIKES DROVE BACK INTO DELIVERANCE.

YOU HAVEN'T SEEN THE *LAST* OF THE RATS... BUT *IF* YOU ERECT SIRENS WELL AWAY FROM THE TOWN, IT'LL *LURE* THEM AWAY.

THEN YOU'LL HAVE ENOUGH FOOD TO EAT — SO MAYBE YOU CAN GO IN FOR MORE *CIVILISED* LAWS IN FUTURE, HUH?

YES, NOW THE LAWGIVER IS *DEAD*, THINGS WILL *CHANGE* AROUND HERE. WE ARE IN YOUR DEBT, JUDGE.

AS DREDD AND SPIKES DROVE BACK TO THE WAITING LAND-RAIDER...

YOU KNOW, JUDGEY — THE REASON I DELAYED RESCUING YOU WAS 'COS I WAS LOOKING ROUND DELIVERANCE... CAME ACROSS A *COUPLE OF INTERESTING ITEMS.*

WHEN WE GET INSIDE, I'LL SHOW YOU...

I CAN *HARDLY* WAIT!

GENUINE WORLD WAR TWO *HAND GRENADES* AND A *COLT SIX SHOOTER.* HOW D'YOU LIKE ME? D'YOU THINK I LOOK CUTE...LIKE ONE OF DEM TWENTIETH CENTURY *PUNK ROCKERS?*

YOU — ER — LOOK *WONDERFUL,* SPIKES!

AS THE LAND-RAIDER CONTINUED ITS PERILOUS JOURNEY...

BACK TO BUSINESS, GENTLEMEN... WE'VE OVERCOME THE DEVIL'S LAPDOGS — BUT EVEN *WORSE* DANGERS AWAIT US. WE HAVEN'T MET *THE MUTIES, THE WHIPPER-SNAPPERS,* OR *THE SLAY-RIDERS...* YET!

NEXT PROG:

THE MUTIE MOUNTAINS!

33

THIS IS MUTIE COUNTRY!

2000 A.D. Credit Card:
SCRIPT ROBOT PAT MILLS
ART ROBOT BRIAN BOLLAND
LETTERING ROBOT TOM FRAME
COMPU·73E

BUT, MEANWHILE, A NONE TOO FRIENDLY FACE WAS WATCHING THE LAND-RAIDER...

THAT'S WHY WE'RE GOING OVER THE MOUNTAINS, SPIKES...THIS IS A MISSION OF MERCY — NOT MURDER! I WISH THOSE CRAZY DEVILS NO HARM.

SET A NEW COURSE, JUDGE GRADGRIND!

BROTHER MORGAR MUST HEAR OF THIS....!

THE MUTANT SPED BACK TOWARDS THE CITY...

HO! HO!

IN A SUPERMARKET IN THE RUINED CITY... BROTHER MORGAR, LEADER OF THE BROTHERHOOD OF DARKNESS...

BROTHERS OBEE AND JOBEE... TASTE THIS FOOD THAT HAS BEEN DISCOVERED — TO MAKE SURE IT WILL NOT POISON YOUR LEADER...

MMMM BAKED BEANS — VINTAGE TWENTIETH CENTURY... A RARE AND JUICY DELICACY, BROTHER MORGAR.

IS GOOD... VERY GOOD...

ALL RIGHT, THAT'S ENOUGH... YOU'RE JUST MEANT TO TASTE IT!

AH, BROTHER GOMORRAH, WHAT NEWS DO YOU BRING US?

AFTER THE MUTANT HAD EXPLAINED...

SO... A PARTY OF NORMS CROSSING OUR SACRED MOUNTAINS... DEFILING THEM! REMEMBER, O MY BROTHERS, THE VOW WE MADE ON THE DAY WE CRAWLED OUT FROM THE FALL OUT... ALL NORMS MUST DIE! THEY MUST NOT ESCAPE!

MEANWHILE...

THE CANNON'S BLASTING A WAY UP THE MOUNTAIN... BUT THERE'S ONLY OLD TOURIST PATHS PAST THE FACES OF THE PRESIDENTS... THEY CAN'T TAKE A BATTLE WAGON LIKE THIS!

WE'LL SEE. I'LL RIDE SHOTGUN. HOLD HER STEADY, JUDGE GRADGRIND

SUDDENLY...

DEATH TO THE NORMS!

AAAHZ-ZZzzz.

DREDD! THAT THING... IT'S SLASHED RIGHT THROUGH THE ROOF!

THE MUTANTS HAVE GOT A "LA-SAW" MOBILE.... THE MACHINE 21st CENTURY SCULPTORS USED TO CARVE PRESIDENT CARTER'S FACE.

FULL SPEED... ACTIVATE ALL GUNS!

DAT MUST BE HOW DA MUTIES MADE THE FACE OF THEIR LEADER! AND NOW THEY'RE GONNA DO SOME MORE CARVING...

...ON US!

AIEEEE! LET DARKNESS TRIUMPH OVER LIGHT!

"OUR SHELLS HAVE NO EFFECT ON THOSE LASER BLADES! THEY'LL CUT US TO BITS..."

THANK YOU, JUDGE GRADGRIND...

DREDD TO BOTH MODULE COMMANDERS... ADOPT SEPARATION PROCEDURE... READY TO ACTIVATE...

...NOW!

THE KILLDOZER SLAMMED ON ITS BRAKES, AND THE RAIDER CAR DISENGAGED AND LEAPED FORWARD.

BY STOMM! WE DID IT—BUT THE ROAD'S SMASHED TO BITS...

WE CAN'T RE-DOCK WITH THE RAIDER CAR... IT'S ON ITS OWN!

AND LOOK WHAT'S HEADING TOWARDS IT!

"... DA WHOLE OF DA MUTIE BRUDDERHOOD!"

THE DAY OF ATONEMENT IS AT HAND!

YEAH — BUT RIGHT NOW — OUR *FRIEND* IN THAT FLYING BUZZ SAW IS COMING IN FOR *THE KILL*...

IF MY SLUG HITS THE LASER BLADES... *WE'VE HAD IT*!

GOT TO AIM *PAST* THEM... IN *AT THE PILOT*...

EEEEUGH!

THE LA-SAW SPUN CRAZILY OUT OF CONTROL...

NO! NO! NOT... THE TEETH!

AAAGH!

GOOD SHOOTING, JUDGEY!

THE RAIDER CAR — LOADED WITH THE *VITAL VACCINE* — IS STILL AT THE MUTANTS MERCY!

NO WAY WE CAN HELP THEM! *UNLESS*...

THE BOFFINS TELL US THE KILLDOZER IS CAPABLE OF *CLIMBING ANY TERRAIN*... OKAY — LET'S PUT IT TO THE *TEST*...

WE'RE GONNA CLIMB— *THE HEIGHTS OF ABRAHAM!*

SO...

COME ON... THE KILLDOZER'S STARTING TO SLIP... PUT HER IN A *LOWER GEAR*!

BUT, JUDGE... SHE'S IN *BOTTOM GEAR* ALREADY!

KEEP *ROOTING* FOR US, *ABE* BABY!

MEANWHILE...

THE NORMS HAVE *SURRENDERED*, BROTHER MORGAR. THEY REALISED THEY WERE *POWERLESS* TO RESIST!

IT IS WELL DONE. A MUTIE ALWAYS GETS HIS MAN.

DESTROY THEIR CARGO AND TAKE THE NORMS TO THE *PLACE OF EXECUTION*... BENEATH MY SACRED STATUE... AND THERE, *NORM BLOOD SHALL FLOW*...

HAIL, BROTHER MORGAR! LET THE WEEPING, GNASHING OF TEETH, AND *ALL THAT JAZZ,* BEGIN!

AYE! THE DAY OF ATONEMENT IS AT HAND!

WRONG! THE DAY OF JUDGEMENT IS AT HAND!

THE OTHER NORMS... H–HOW DID THEY GET *HERE* ?

QUICKLY—BROTHERS OBEE AND JOBEE...*SAVE YOUR LEADER!* THE REST OF YOU... *KILL THE NORMS!*

JUDGE DREDD SPEAKS...

WAIT! RELEASE MY MEN AND THEIR MACHINE, MORGAR... OR MY KILLDOZER WILL DO SOME *INSTANT SURGERY* ON THAT STATUE OF YOURS...

LIKE BLOWING ITS NOSE... *RIGHT OFF!*

AND THEN ADDING *ANOTHER EYE*... IN THE MIDDLE OF *DA FOREHEAD!* AND YOU AIN'T GOT NO "LA-SAW" NOW TO MAKE YA FACE LOOK *PRETTY AGAIN!*

NO...TH–THEY MUST NOT DESTROY MY STATUE... DO AS THEY SAY, BROTHERS, *RELEASE THE PRISONERS!*

SO, THE LAND RAIDER CONTINUES ITS PERILOUS JOURNEY. ON THE COMMAND BRIDGE...

DA MUTIES HAVE LET US GO FOR NOW... BUT MORGAR'S BEEN MADE TO LOOK *STUPID* IN FRONT OF *DA BRUDDERHOOD*...

HE'LL BE *AFTER US* — *THIRSTING FOR OUR BLOOD!* WE SHOULDA *DESTROYED* 'EM ALL WHEN WE HAD THE CHANCE!

SICK, CRAZY MUTANTS... THEY DESERVE *PITY*, SPIKES — *NOT VENGEANCE*... A JUDGE MUST BE *STERN*, BUT HE MUST ALSO SHOW *MERCY*...

THAT IS THE FACE OF JUSTICE!

NEXT PROG : DARK AUTUMN!

WHAT VILE MADNESS IS GRIPPING THESE PEOPLE?

DREDD

Prog 66

2000 A.D.

27 MAY 78 IN ORBIT EVERY MONDAY

9p EARTH MONEY

South Africa 30c
New Zealand 30c
Australia $1.00
Malaysia 17c
Mercury 17c
Venus 15c
Mars 18c
Asteroid Belt 24c
Neptune 87c
Pluto 93c

I THINK I SMELL A RAT!

THE CURSED EARTH CHAPTER 6. DARK AUTUMN!

JUDGE DREDD

THE LAND-RAIDER — WITH JUDGE DREDD AND HIS SPECIAL COMBAT TEAM — CONTINUES ITS JOURNEY TOWARDS MEGA-CITY TWO, ACROSS THE CURSED EARTH — THE STRETCH OF DESERT LEFT OVER FROM THE ATOMIC WARS . . .

THE BROTHERHOOD ARE STILL ON OUR TRACKS, BUT THE LAND-RAIDER IS EQUIPPED WITH ALL THE LATEST WAR WEAPONS JUDGE DREDD.

ONE WAY

2000 A.D. Credit Card:
SCRIPT ROBOT PAT MILLS
ART ROBOT MIKE McMAHON
LETTERING ROBOT TOM FRAME
COMPU-73E

44

46

54

BUT WHAT WE'RE LOOKING FOR IS *HIDDEN* DOWN IN THE VAULTS! *COME ON!* I THINK I KNOW THE ANSWER TO THE MYSTERY!

DOWN INSIDE THE FORT, GOLD BULLION WAS STILL STORED...

BOY! *LOOK AT ALL DIS GOLD,* JUDGEY! HEY, WHY DON'T WE...

FORGET IT, SPIKES! WHAT WE'RE AFTER IS *EVEN MORE VALUABLE!* SPREAD OUT, EVERYONE— AND LOOK FOR A *SECRET ENTRANCE* TO THE VAULT BELOW!

SUDDENLY...

HELLO, INTRUDERS... HOW ARE YOU...? NOW DON'T...

...THINK WE'RE BEING RUDE, BUT WE'RE GOING TO HAVE TO... ...KILL YOU! ...ORDERS, YOU...

MEDIC ROBOTS! WITH A COLLECTIVE PERSONALITY — BUT CAPABLE OF *INDEPENDENT* ACTION! *BLAST 'EM!*

...KNOW, IF THERE'S *ANY...*

...WAY WE CAN *MAKE* IT...

...*EASIER* FOR YOU. WE'D BE...

BULLETS HAVE NO EFFECT ON THE METAL VAMPS... QUICK, SPIKES — ABOUT TURN!

...HAPPY TO *OBLIGE!* AFTER ALL, THAT'S...

...WHAT ROBOTS ARE FOR... DON'T YOU...

...THINK?

HEAVE, SPIKES! *HEAVE!*

THE CURSED EARTH

CHAPTER 8.

THE SLEEPER AWAKES!

JUDGE DREDD

ON THE WILD HILLBILLY TERRITORY OF KENTUCKY, A STRANGE VAMPIRE HAS BEEN ATTACKING AND DRAINING ITS VICTIMS OF THEIR LIFE BLOOD.

THE HILLBILLIES APPEAL TO JUDGE DREDD FOR HELP, AND A SEARCH LEADS TO THE VAULTS OF RUINED FORT KNOX, WHERE . . .

IN THE VAULT . . .

THIS BE THE VAMPIRE . . .

. . . GOTTA RAM THE STAKE RIGHT THROUGH ITS BLACK HEART !

DROKK IT! THE HILLBILLIES ARE GOING TO .KILL . . .

THE LAST PRESIDENT OF THE UNITED STATES !

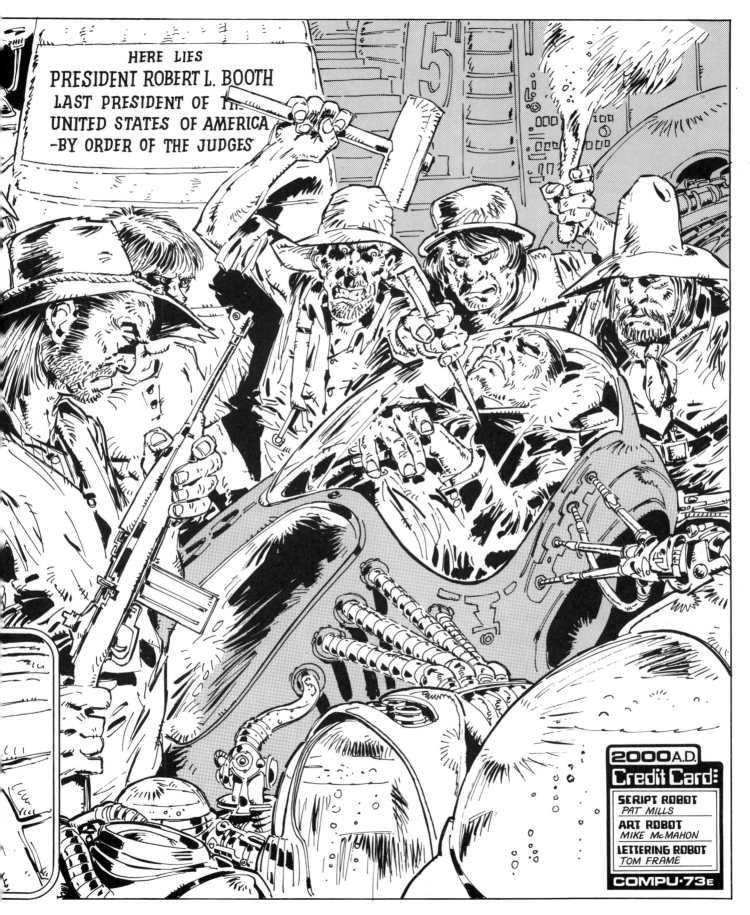

"ONLY THE JUDGES COULD COME UP WITH A SENTENCE THAT WAS *FAIR* ... THE FAMOUS "*JUDGEMENT OF SOLOMON*" !

MR. PRESIDENT, WE SENTENCE YOU TO ... *ONE HUNDRED YEARS SUSPENDED ANIMATION!*

YOU WILL BE TAKEN FROM HERE TO *FORT KNOX* — FOR *PROTECTION* — AND *THERE*, YOUR BODY FROZEN AND STORED IN THE DEEPEST VAULT !

"AT FORT KNOX — THREE MEDIC ROBOTS — *SPECIALLY PROGRAMMED,* LOOKED AFTER THE PRESIDENT..."

"YEAR AFTER YEAR...THEY FAITHFULLY CHECKED AND *CHANGED* HIS BLOOD..."

"UNTIL THE DAY A BOMB HIT FORT KNOX —AND ONLY THE PRESIDENT AND THE ROBOTS WERE LEFT ALIVE..."

THERE'S NO MORE BLOOD. BUT WE MUST OBEY OUR PROGRAMMING.... WE MUST *SEARCH* FOR... ...*MORE* !

THAT'S HOW THE *LEGEND* OF THE *VAMPIRE* GREW IN THESE PARTS...

ROBOTS WHO WERE TRYING TO KEEP THEIR PRESIDENT *ALIVE* — THE *ONLY* WAY THEY KNEW HOW. COME AND MEET... "*SNAP*", "*CRACKLE*" AND "*POP*".

DREDD LED THEM TO THE FLOOR ABOVE...

I'M AFRAID IT'S *TRUE.* WE... ...DID GO AROUND "*DRINKING*" EVERYONE'S MOTION LOTION.

AND WE'D LIKE TO APOLOGISE !

SO *YOU* BE THE ONE'S WHO *KILLED* MY DAUGHTER !

WAIT! THAT WON'T BRING HER BACK, IKKABOD ...BUT "*SNAP*", "*CRACKLE*" AND "*POP*" CAN BE *MENDED* AND *REPROGRAMMED* TO *WORK FOR YOU*... THAT MAKES A LOT MORE *SENSE* !

THE JUDGE IS *RIGHT*... THERE'S BEEN *ENOUGH* FEUDIN'...

THE SLAY-RIDERS!

JUDGE DREDD

JUDGE'S LOG . . . . DAY TWELVE
JOURNEY CO-ORDINATES A7..L5..3.
TODAY WE CROSS THE MISSISSIPPI,
CONTINUING OUR JOURNEY TO MEGA-CITY TWO.
THE ONCE MIGHTY RIVER IS STILL ABLAZE
WITH PETROL, FOUL-SMELLING
POLLUTANTS, AND NUCLEAR WASTES FROM
THE DAYS OF THE GREAT ATOMIC WAR.
IT HAS BECOME — A TORRENT
OF FIERY DEATH!

AS THE LAND RAIDER REACHED THE OTHER SIDE AND LOADED UP WITH PROVISIONS...

SURE IS GOOD TO SEE SOME *HUMAN* FACES AGAIN... SPECIALLY A *MEGA-CITY LAWMAN* LIKE YOURSELF, JUDGE DREDD. WE'VE HEARD OF YOU — *EVEN* IN THESE PARTS.

THAT *IS* HOW IT SHOULD BE, FERRY-MASTER. BUT *HOW* DID YOU COME BY ALL THESE ALIENS?

SPECIMENS BROUGHT BACK BY THE STARSHIPS... USED TO BE KEPT ON AN *ALIEN NATURE RESERVE* NEAR HERE...

BUT THEN THE WAR CAME AND *EVERYTHING* CHANGED. ME AND SOME OF THE OTHER LOCALS *BOUGHT 'EM UP CHEAP.*

AND USED THEM AS *SLAVE LABOUR.* YOUR TRADE *SICKENS* ME TO MY GUTS, FERRY-MASTER.

NOW — ER — DON'T START FEELING *SORRY* FOR 'EM, JUDGE. THEY *AIN'T* INTELLIGENT.

SEE THAT FURRY ONE... *HE EATS ROCKS!* CAN YOU THINK OF *ANYTHING DUMBER?*

SHEESH, JUDGEY... I'D HAVE A *HELLUVA* BELLY-ACHE IF I EAT GRANITE STEAKS LIKE *FREAK-FACE.*

HAW, HAW! THE STUPID BEAST'S REAL *CHEAP* TO FEED... I GIVE 'IM A COUPLE O' BOULDERS A DAY AN' HE WORKS *HARDER* THAN A GANG OF ROBO-NAVVIES.

MAYBE HE FINDS THE WAY HUMANS EAT OTHER ANIMALS *JUST AS STUPID.*

SUDDENLY...

LOOK OUT, JUDGE — THE BRUTE CAN *CRACK YOUR SKULL IN HALF* WITH THOSE PINCERS!

TWURP!

THE CURSED EARTH
CHAPTER 10

REQUIEM FOR AN ALIEN!

JUDGE DREDD

HOLD ON TO YOUR FUR, TWEAK — WE GOTTA GET THROUGH THEM NAPALM THROWERS!

TWOKK?

THE SLAY RIDER'S COMING IN FOR THE FINISH — AND TWEAK'S FUR IS ALREADY ALIGHT...

TWEAK! TWEAK! TWEAK!

2000 A.D.
Credit Card:

SCRIPT ROBOT
PAT MILLS

ART ROBOT
BRIAN BOLLAND

LETTERING ROBOT
TOM FRAME

COMPU-73E

AAAAGH!

MEANWHILE...

TWALK...?

"THE DUMB BRUTE'S AT OUR MERCY NOW...HE CAN'T CONTROL THAT MACHINE!"

UNKNOWINGLY, THE ALIEN HAD PRESSED THE AUTO-MORTAR SWITCH...

AND...

TWURP... TWURP?

AIEEE

?

TWAAAW!

NOW!

NO! NOT... THE POWER SWORD!

YOU BIT OFF MORE THAN YOU COULD CHEW, PAL!

THE BATTLE WAS OVER... THE MEN FROM MEGA-CITY COUNTED THE COST...

JUDGE PATTON DEAD... MOST OF THE ROBOTS SMASHED... AND FOR WHAT? TO SAVE THE LIFE OF SOME DUMB ALIEN!

QUIT BUGGIN' ME, SPIKES! WHEN I SWORE MY JUDGE'S OATH, I SWORE IT TO PROTECT EVERYONE!

WHERE'S FREAK FACE GOING?

HE'S HEADING INTO THAT PLANTATION — LOOK AT HIM MOVE!

TWEAK!

HE'S PUTTING ROCKS ON... A GRAVE!

THEN THE SLAY-RIDERS WERE RIGHT... TWEAK IS A KILLER! HE KILLED SOME INNOCENT HUMANS AND NOW HE'S TRYING TO HIDE THE EVIDENCE...

ONLY HE'S SO DUMB — HE'S LED US TO THE SCENE OF HIS CRIME!

TWEAK, AIN'T MUCH I CAN DO TO MAKE AMENDS, BUDDY... BUT YOU'RE WELCOME TO COME WITH US. AND — *I'M SORRY.*

FILL IN THE GRAVE !

TWOLK !

WH-WHAT WAS IN THE GRAVE ?

THREE ALIENS — LIKE TWEAK, TWO OF THEM *SMALL* — AND THE OTHER WITH GOLDEN FUR... YEAH, TWEAK'S MATE AND KIDS...*SHOT* — BY HUMAN BULLETS !

THAT'S WHY TWEAK ESCAPED — SO HE COULD REACH THIS PLANTATION WHERE THEY WERE SLAVES — SO HE COULD SEE HIS *FAMILY* AGAIN...

MY GUESS IS THE PLANTATION OWNER — ONE OF THE SLAY-RIDERS — FOUND THEY DIDN'T WORK HARD ENOUGH — *AND HAD THEM SHOT...*

SO TWEAK BURIED THEM AND BEGAN LAYING ROCKS ON THEIR GRAVE..."FOOD" FOR THEIR JOURNEY AFTER DEATH — ACCORDING TO THE *CUSTOM* ON HIS PLANET... AND *WE'RE* GONNA HELP HIM...!

AND SO...

: TWURRRRP :

I THINK TWEAK'S TRYING TO TELL YOU, SPIKES — HE ONLY LIKES THE HARD STUFF... GRANITE AND QUARTZ !

SHEESH ! HE'S REALLY *FUSSY* ABOUT HIS GRUB — AND I LUGGED THESE NICE JUICY ROCKS ALL THE WAY UP THE HILL SPECIAL.

THEY LEFT TWEAK ALONE FOR A FEW MINUTES BY THE GRAVE ...

DRAGGED AS A SPECIMEN OFF HIS HOME PLANET... *SOLD* INTO SLAVERY...HIS MATE AND KIDS *BUTCHERED* ON A WORLD LIGHT YEARS AWAY FROM HOME ... YEAH, TWEAK MUST *REALLY* THINK WE HUMANS ARE *CIVILISED* !

THE LAND-RAIDER CONTINUED ITS DANGEROUS JOURNEY TO MEGA-CITY TWO, ACROSS THE CURSED EARTH ...

JUDGE DREDD'S LOG :
DAY THIRTEEN
JOURNEY CO-ORDINATES : A9–L6. 8.

SOMETIMES THE HUMAN RACE MAKES ME SICK !

JUDGE DREDD WILL RETURN IN PART 2 OF THE CURSED EARTH.